KC-135 Stratotank

in action

by C. M. Reed
Color by Don Greer
Illustrated by Joe Sewell

Aircraft Number 118
squadron/signal publications

A KC-135A Stratotanker of the 379th Bomb Wing based at Wurtsmith AFB, Michigan, refuels a Boeing B-52 Stratofortress bomber. The primary mission of the Stratotankers in SAC is to support the B-52/B-1 bomber fleets.

ISBN 0-89747-268-3

If you have any photographs of the aircraft, armor, soldiers or ships of any nation, particularly wartime snapshots, why not share them with us and help make Squadron/Signal's books all the more interesting and complete in the future. Any photograph sent to us will be copied and the original returned. The donor will be fully credited for any photos used. Please send them to:

Squadron/Signal Publications, Inc.
1115 Crowley Drive.
Carrollton, TX 75011-5010.

Photo Credits

U.S. Air Force
Boeing
Bill E. Harkins
Nicholas J. Waters III
French Air Force

Simon N.J. Edwards
General Dynamics
Larry Davis
Terry Love

Acknowledgements

I would like to thank all the people who helped, in one way or another, to make this book possible. A lot of folks were very generous with their aid and I certainly appreciate it. A special mention must be made of the contributions by Simon N.J. Edwards, Antoine J. Givaudon, Bill E. Harkins, MSGT Earl Berlin and CAPT Brian C. Rogers.

Thanks must also go to the Public Affairs personnel of the following Air Force units, who gracefully put up with my many requests for information.

189th TAG
22nd ARW
384th BMW
321st SMW
443rd MAW
28th BMW
28th AD
55th WRS
55th SRW
9th SRW
HQ SAC 305th ARW

410th BMW
509th BMW
7th BMW
438th MAW
42nd BMW
96th BMW
380th BMW
379th BMW
57th AD
HQ TAC 15th ABW

This KC-135A (56-3593) was assigned to the 189th Air Refueling Group, Arkansas Air National Guard. This unit later converted to the KC-135E before becoming a Tactical Airlift Group equipped with C-130Es. (189th TAG/USAF)

Author's Note:

It should be stated that despite their similarity, the KC-135 and the Boeing Model 707 airliner are not military and commercial sides of the same coin (although they do share some common parts), but are two different types. No attempt has been made in this work to chronicle the numerous military variants of the Boeing 707.

Introduction

When the last Boeing KC-135 Stratotanker is finally retired, sometime in the 21st century, the aircraft will have achieved a record as one of the most versatile and long-lived designs in the history of military aviation. Designed primarily as a refueling tanker for the Strategic Air Command, the KC-135 has served as the basis for over forty variants, serving in such roles as transport, electronic reconnaissance, airborne command post, and radio relay, among others. Unlike many of its contemporaries, the KC-135A remains in service and is likely to remain in service for years to come. The same Stratotanker that refueled B-47s and B-52s in the late 1950s may very well be refueling B-2 Stealth bombers and F-23 ATFs during the 1990s.

In-flight refueling can be traced back to June of 1923, when the first airborne transfer of fuel occurred. Two DH-4 biplanes were used: the tanker aircraft trailing a fuel hose/cable that was physically grabbed by the crew of the receiver aircraft. Using this method, the receiver managed to stay aloft for over thirty-seven hours. This feat soon inspired other record-breaking endurance flights. During January of 1929, the Atlantic-Fokker C-2A, named "Question Mark," made a 150 hour, 11,000 mile flight. During 1935, a Curtiss Robin flew a four week long circuit around an airport in Mississippi. On such flights, engine oil and food also had to be transferred in addition to fuel.

Boeing was a pioneer in this field, with the "Boeing Hornet Shuttle." This aircraft was a Model 95 biplane which could take on fuel from Model 40B tankers. The aircraft made two non-stop, in-flight refueled trips across the United States, delivering mail from California to New York and vice-versa. The project ended when the Model 95 crashed on the second trip eastward.

In the 1930s, with the growing acceptance of air travel, in-flight refueling was investigated as a means of increasing the range of passenger aircraft on the long Atlantic and Pacific routes. A number of experiments were carried out, such as the refueled transatlantic flights of Imperial Air Lines Short C-class flying boats during 1939. The Second World War II put a halt to such civil programs.

During the war, various proposals for equipping military aircraft for in-flight refueling were made, but little came of these. After the war, further commercial tests were carried out by the British, with Liberators (B-24s) being refueled by Lancaster tankers. The arrival of long-range airliners ended the need for passenger aircraft to take on fuel while airborne.

It was the Cold War that finally brought in-flight refueling into widespread use. During the period immediately following the Second World War, the manned bomber was the sole means of delivering nuclear weapons over long distances. The Strategic Air Command was the first operator of nuclear-armed strategic bombers, but faced the problem of reaching Soviet targets. The B-29 did not have the range to effectively hit the USSR from bases in the continental US and SAC viewed in-flight refueling as a means of extending the range of the bombers and escort fighters.

The first refueling method employed by the USAF was the hose and grapple system developed by the British firm of Flight Refueling, Ltd. This system consisted of a cable reeled out behind the tanker, which was grabbed by a grappling hook trailed by the receiver. The cable was brought aboard the receiver and a fuel hose was reeled out from the tanker to the receiver. The hose and grapple system was fitted to the first USAF tanker, the KB-29M, which went into service during 1948. By the time the hose and grapple system was entering service, a better refueling method was already being tested.

During 1947, the Air Material Command had contracted Boeing to work on an improved in-flight refueling system, which emerged as the Boeing Flying Boom. Totally different from any other system, the Flying Boom was precisely what its name implied: a metal boom that an operator could steer via aerodynamic control surfaces on the boom itself. SAC adopted the boom, fitting it to 116 B-29s which were redesignated as KB-29P tankers. B-50 Superfortress IIs were equipped as receivers.

Across the Atlantic, Flight Refueling Ltd. was also working on a next generation refueling system, known as the "probe and drogue" method. The "drogue" part of this system is a flexible fuel line reeled out behind a tanker, with a basket attached to the end of the line. The refueling probe of the receiver aircraft is inserted into the basket and fuel is transferred. Although less controllable than the Flying Boom, the probe and drogue system is perhaps more versatile, since many different aircraft types could be outfitted as drogue tankers. TAC was equipped with 136 KB-50J and KB-50K three-point drogue tankers. TAC eventually lost its independent tanker force, but the U.S. Navy and virtually all foreign air forces with in-flight refueling capability use the probe and drogue system.

In-flight refueling had its baptism of fire during the Korean War. Project Hightide entailed the use of a number of KB-29Ms which had the probe and drogue system, with F-80 Shooting Stars and F-84 Thunderjets as receivers. Although the art of in-flight refueling was still in its infancy, this initial combat application showed the potential for increased range and weapon loads. KB-29Ps also participated during the Korean conflict "dragging" F-84Es across the Pacific and refueling RB-45C Tornado recon aircraft for flights over North Korea.

The KB-29 was replaced by the Boeing KC-97, a variant of the C-97 Stratofreighter. Three KC-97A prototypes were converted, followed by the first production model, the KC-97E. The final new-build model was the KC-97G which had the capability to function as both a tanker and transport simultaneously. 592 KC-97Gs were built before the type was phased out in favor of the first jet tanker, the KC-135.

The KC-135 began as a Boeing effort during the early 1950s to market a jet transport for both military and airline use. Boeing, traditionally a builder of large military aircraft, had tried to break into the postwar airliner market with the Model 377 Stratoliner; however, the type was not popular and only fifty-six were produced.

Officials at Boeing felt that a jet-powered transport might be able to bring in sales both as superior airliner and as a tanker/transport for the USAF. Boeing had the know-how for such a project based on experience gained in the design and manufacture of the B-47 Stratojet medium bomber.

The Boeing piston engined KC-97 was replaced in USAF service by the jet powered KC-135A. For a time, National Guard units like the Illinois Air National Guard, retained their late model KC-97s until sufficient KC-135As were available to re-equip these units. (N.J. Waters III)

Design studies for the new jet were included in the Model 367 series as a clever bit of industrial subterfuge intended to cultivate the belief that the new aircraft was another C-97 variant. One of the interim designs, the Model 367-64, showed a C-97 fuselage mated to swept wings and tail surfaces and powered by four JT3/J57 turbojets in double under-wing pods.

The final design, the Model 367-80, was an entirely new aircraft. The new transport was more streamlined and far longer than its piston-powered predecessor and the wings were swept at 35 degrees (the same as the B-47) with dihedral on both the wings and tailplanes.

The 367-80 was powered by four 11,000 lbst Pratt & Whitney JT3P turbojets mounted in single engine pods suspended on pylons under the wings. This arrangement improved access for maintenance and eliminated the possibility that an explosion of one engine would damage or destroy the engine next to it, as was common on twin engine pods (B-47 and B-52). The aircraft was equipped with a tricycle landing gear with a twin-wheel nose gear and four-wheel main gear.

While Boeing was convinced of the potential of the 367-80, some of its potential customers were not. Airlines were well equipped with modern piston-engined airliners such as the Lockheed Super Constellation and Douglas DC-6. Early Jets had gotten a lot of bad press with the crashes of the early British Comet airliners. As a result, there was little interest in the Boeing design from the commercial sector and Boeing received no advanced orders to assist in financing the project.

Boeing knew, however, that the Air Force would eventually need a faster, higher-flying tanker to better match the performance of the new generation of fighters and bombers coming into service. Convinced that sales to both the military and commercial sectors were possible if an actual 367-80 prototype could be demonstrated, Boeing's president, William Allen, convinced the board of directors, on 20 May 1952, to invest $16 million in the construction of a single Model 367-80 prototype.

The 367-80 prototype, or "Dash Eighty" as it was nicknamed, rolled out from the Boeing plant at Renton, Washington, on 14 May 1954 and made its first flight on 15 July flown by Boeing's chief test pilot, Alvin M. "Tex" Johnson. Although the 367-80 was destined to be the only aircraft of its type, it would serve as the prototype for both the KC-135 tanker/transport and Model 707 airliner, as well as performing valuable test duties until the early 1970s.

Shortly after the first flight of the Dash Eighty, the USAF announced (in August of 1954) that it would purchase twenty-nine Flying Boom-equipped tanker/transports under the designation KC-135. The contract for these initial aircraft (Boeing Model 717-100A), which were given the name Stratotanker, was formalized on 5 October 1954.

Although clearly based on the 367-80, the KC-135 Stratotanker differed from the prototype in a number of ways. It was eight feet three inches longer, the fuselage was twelve inches wider and it weighed over 300,000 pounds.

There were no service test aircraft and the first production KC-135A (55-3118) rolled out from the Renton plant on 20 July 1956. R.L. "Dix" Loesch took 55-3118 on its first flight some two months later, on 31 August and the KC-135 flight test program was begun using the initial production tankers. Christened "City of Renton," this aircraft has it has proved to be long lived. It still remains in service modified to the EC-135K configuration.

The Boeing 367-80 "Dash Eighty" prototype conducts a refueling test with an early B-52 Stratofortress. The prototype was outfitted with a dummy flying boom for simulated refueling tests to determine approach and positioning data. (Boeing)

Development

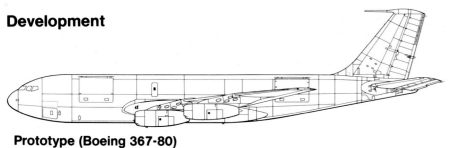

Prototype (Boeing 367-80)

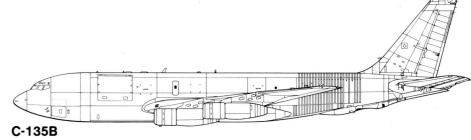

C-135B

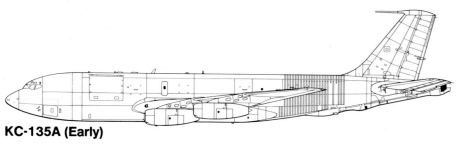

KC-135A (Early)

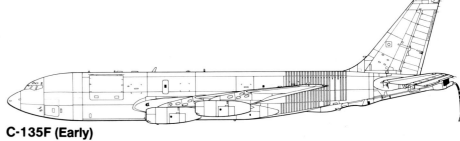

C-135F (Early)

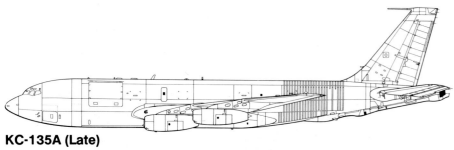

KC-135A (Late)

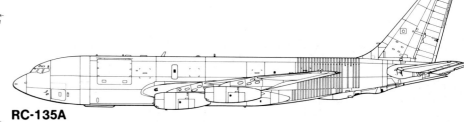

RC-135A

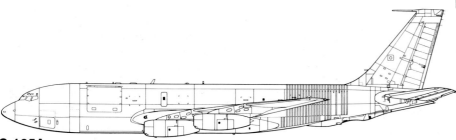

C-135A

Tankers

KC-135A Stratotanker

The KC-135A began its operational career on 30 April 1957, when Boeing delivered the first three production aircraft to the USAF. The first unit to be equipped with the new tanker was the 93rd Air Refueling Squadron at Castle AFB, California. The 93rd began KC-135A operations in June of 1957, less than a year after the first flight of 55-3118. Deliveries of KC-135As from Boeing eventually hit fifteen aircraft per month, due in part to the gradual shift of B-52 production from Renton to the Boeing plant at Wichita.

Unlike the 367-80 prototype, the production KC-135A has a single cargo door on the port side of the forward fuselage. The door opens upward and outward to allow loading of cargo. Typically, a KC-135A Stratotanker can accommodate eighty passengers or up to 41.5 tons of cargo. Various combinations of personnel and cargo can be accommodated.

The Stratotanker has a crew of four: pilot, copilot, navigator and boom operator, commonly known as the "boomer," who also serves as the loadmaster. The heart of the KC-135A is the Flying Boom refueling system operated by the boomer. The system is operated from a pod under the rear fuselage. Access to the pod is gained through an opening in the cabin deck. Once in the pod, the boomer lies on his stomach on a pallet, facing rearwards, with the refueling controls and a window in front of him. There are two additional pallets in the pod (right and left of the operator's pallet) for use by boom instructors, students, or observers.

The Flying Boom is housed against the rear fuselage when not in use and can be raised or lowered with a manual system if the power system should fail. The boom can be moved plus 12.5 degrees and minus 50 degrees in the vertical and 30 degrees horizontal. The KC-135A Stratotanker can be fitted with two types of booms: the "High Speed" type for use at all speeds and the "Standard Speed" boom, which can only be used at speeds up to 330 knots.

A fueling probe is housed within the boom which is telescopically extended to make contact with the receiving aircraft's refueling receptacle. The tip of the probe has a valve which is opened once the probe has been locked into the receiver's receptacle.

To guide pilots of receiver aircraft, KC-135As were equipped with two rows of director lights under the forward fuselage. Early KC-135s had a fluorescent Yellow stripe applied to the underside of the fuselage as an aid in the longitudinal alignment of receivers. This was later deleted.

The KC-135A has a great fuel capacity, both for transfer and for its own use. The wings each house two fuel tanks: the inboard tank has a capacity of 2,275 gallons while the outboard tank has a capacity of 2,062 gallons. Additionally, a 434 gallon reserve tank is mounted outboard of the main tanks in both wings and a 7,306 gallon tank is housed in the wing center section.

Within the fuselage, there are nine fuel cells under the cabin floor. The four forward cells have a capacity of 5,800 gallons, while the five rear cells hold a total of 6,378 gallons. There is a 2,174 gallon tank mounted in the rear of the cabin. Fuselage fuel is normally used for refueling purposes, while wing fuel is used for the tanker. The total fuel load is 31,200 gallons, virtually all of which can be transferred (alternatively, the tanker itself can burn all fuel carried).

The KC-135A is equipped with an inboard "all speed" aileron on each wing, between the inboard and outboard flaps and outboard "low speed" ailerons which can only be operated when the flaps are in use. A pair of spoilers are mounted in front of each flap on the wing uppersurface. These spoilers enhance roll control when used differentially and can also be used as speed brakes. The aircraft is also equipped with trailing edge Fowler type flaps and an adjustable horizontal stabilizer.

The KC-135A was powered by four 13,750 lbst Pratt & Whitney J57-P-43WB or J57-P-59 non-afterburning turbojets with water/methanol injection for improved takeoff performance. The J57 engines gave the KC-135A a speed of 610 mph, a ceiling of 45,000 feet and a range of 9,942 miles. Despite the use of water/methanol injection, the restricted power of the J57s have limited fully loaded KC-135s to long (13,000+ feet), hard surfaced runways.

Because the U.S. Navy and many allied air forces used the probe and drogue method of refueling, an adapter kit was developed for use with the KC-135. This kit converts the Flying Boom to a drogue/basket unit. The adapter is some thirteen feet long and weighs some 121 pounds. With the adapter in place, the boom cannot be used for normal refueling. KC-135s fitted with drogue units participated in refueling tests of the French Mirage IVA bomber, which led the French Air Force to later purchase a number of KC-135s.

Access to the aircraft is provided by an entry hatch located alongside the nosewheel on the port side of the aircraft. For emergency exit, there are a pair of escape hatches located on either side of the fuselage above the wing, with an additional escape hatch located further back on the starboard side.

The cockpit houses the three-person flight crew, plus a jump-seat for an observer. To allow for better visibility of other aircraft traffic while flying in traffic patterns, there are "eyebrow" windows located above the main cockpit windows. On early production Stratotankers, celestial observations were made through cabin roof windows. Late production KC-135As have had inertial/doppler navigation systems installed and a Fuel Saving Advisor/Cockpit Avionics System (FSA-CAS) which coordinates and displays information concerning navigation, aircraft performance, and fuel management.

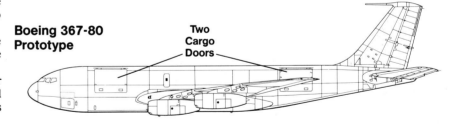

Boeing 367-80 Prototype — Two Cargo Doors

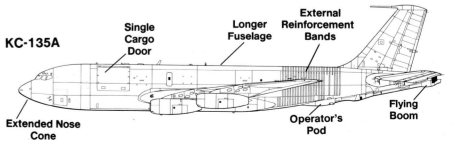

KC-135A — Single Cargo Door, Longer Fuselage, External Reinforcement Bands, Extended Nose Cone, Operator's Pod, Flying Boom

There are two UHF blade antennas mounted above the forward fuselage and a probe antenna for high frequency communications is mounted on the leading edge of the upper fin. An HF wire aerial runs from the fin to the top of the fuselage and antennas for the VOR radio navigation system and the AN/APN-69 radar beacon are built into the fin. A weather radar antenna is carried in the nose behind a small radome.

The first 582 KC-135As off the production line were fitted with short vertical fins and unpowered rudders. To improve directional stability, the fin was extended some forty inches and the rudder was modified with a power boost system. Aircraft 62-3532 was the first KC-135 with the modified fin and rudder, although the change has been retrofitted to most early KC-135As.

Beginning in 1975, the entire Stratotanker force was modified with new lower wing skins under the ECP 405 program. This modification program increased the expected lifespan of the KC-135 fleet to some 26,000 flight hours. At one point, it was planned to retrofit all KC-135s with Whitcomb winglets (tested on NKC-135A 55-3129) as a fuel-saving measure, but this modification was not approved. At least seven KC-135As have refueling receivers installed. These aircraft were former EC/RC-135s that retained their refueling receivers after being reconverted to KC-135A tankers. Another retrofit modification introduced a rear facing floodlight on the top of the vertical fin for night refuelings.

It is planned to modify both the French and U.S. Stratotankers with underwing mounted hose and drogue units, in order to allow refueling of up to three aircraft at a time. This modification would especially be useful for the French, who have a limited tanker fleet.

All KC-135s produced were delivered as KC-135As (except for seventeen KC-135B command post/tankers, which were redesignated as EC-135C/Js upon delivery). KC-135 tanker assets are all assigned to SAC, except those operated by the Air National Guard and Air Force Reserve, although these aircraft would become part of the SAC force if mobilized. The Oklahoma Air Logistics Center at Tinker AFB (Oklahoma City) provided logistical support for the KC-135A/C-135A family and the J57 and TF33 engines. Crew training is carried out at Castle AFB.

During 1975, the Air National Guard began to receive Stratotankers, which allowed the ANG's aging KC-97s to be retired. Eventually, some thirteen ANG squadrons were equipped with the Stratotanker. The Air Force Reserve also received KC-135s, albeit on a smaller scale, equipping three squadrons.

KC-135As were initially delivered in a metallic Corogard Silver finish, although this was later replaced by an overall Light ADC Gray scheme, with the SAC sash and crest carried on the center section of the upper fuselage. With the current emphasis on low-level operations, some KC-135s have received a camouflage scheme similar to that found on the KC-10 Extender.

Stratotankers have also contributed to the U.S. space program, with the type being used to simulate the weightless condition of space by flying parabolic trajectories. This technique has been used for astronaut training and various microgravity experiments. The current "Weightless Wonder/Vomit Comet" aircraft is 59-1481, which is operated by NASA under the civil registration of N930NA from Ellington AFB, Texas. NKC-135s and C-135A 60-0378 have also been used in this role.

The *City of Renton* was the first production KC-153A (55-3118) Stratotanker. The aircraft carried special photographic markings on the fuselage during test flights. The aircraft is still in service reconfigured as an EC-135K. (Boeing)

A KC-135A Stratotanker of the 509th BMW. The Black outlines on the wing uppersurface revealed the location of the wing box, which housed wing fuel tanks. (509th BMW)

The Federal Aviation Administration (FAA) has used the KC-135, the agency being lent two aircraft (59-1518, 59-1481), for navaids testing and other duties. These were given the civil registrations N96 and N98.

Because of Air Force worldwide commitments, there are several forward bases which host CONUS-based tankers on temporarily deployments. The European Tanker Task Force is based at RAF Mildenhall and RAF Fairford in the United Kingdom while another European forward base was Zaragoza AB, in Spain. KC-135s are assigned to the Alaskan Tanker Task Forces and the Alaskan Air National Guard to refuel F-15 fighters for interceptions of Soviet Bear G and Bear H bombers. In the Pacific, KC-135s regularly deploy to Anderson AFB, on the island of Guam.

Foreign sales of the C-135 series were restricted to France (twelve C-135Fs). A proposed sale of used KC-135s to Saudi Arabia, to provide tanker support for RSAF F-15s and E-3s, was considered during the early 1980s, but the Saudis opted for the KE-3A tanker derivative of the E-3 instead.

Deliveries of KC-135As to the USAF ended in January of 1965, when the 732nd KC-135A (64-14840) was delivered to the 380th ARS.

This early production SAC KC-135A (56-3644), in flight with the refueling boom lowered and the fuel probe fully extended, has the later style extended fin and powered rudder. (438th MAW)

An early production KC-135A refuels an RF-101 Voodoo reconnaissance aircraft. This aircraft has the early style short fin and unpowered rudder. It was later retrofitted with the taller fin and powered rudder. (John Fietze)

Vertical Fin

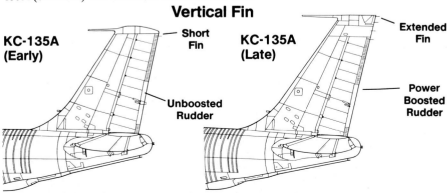

KC-135A (Early) — Short Fin — Unboosted Rudder

KC-135A (Late) — Extended Fin — Power Boosted Rudder

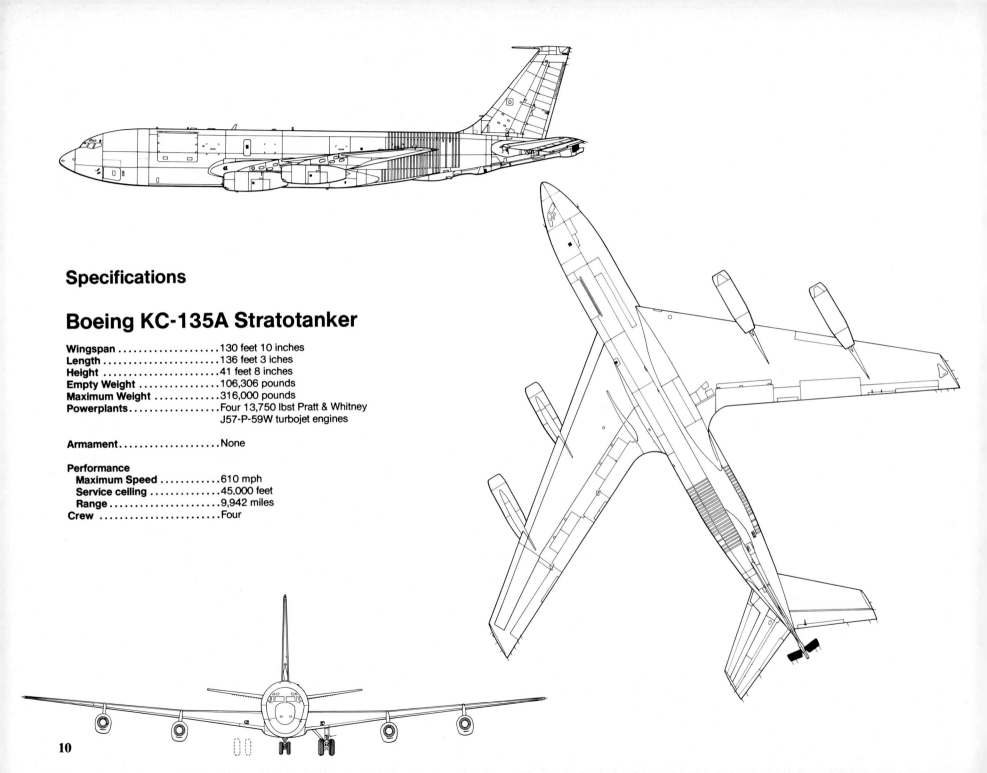

Specifications

Boeing KC-135A Stratotanker

Wingspan .130 feet 10 inches
Length . . . . .136 feet 3 iches
Height . . . . .41 feet 8 inches
Empty Weight . . . . .106,306 pounds
Maximum Weight . . . . .316,000 pounds
Powerplants . . . . .Four 13,750 lbst Pratt & Whitney
J57-P-59W turbojet engines

Armament .None

Performance
  Maximum Speed . . . . .610 mph
  Service ceiling . . . . .45,000 feet
  Range . . . . .9,942 miles
Crew . . . . .Four

A KC-135A on the ramp at Carswell AFB, Fort Worth, Texas. The large concrete objects behind the Stratotanker are jet blast deflectors designed to protect the B-52s behind the KC-135 from jet exhaust. (7th BMW)

This KC-135A (60-0333) was part of the 380th Bombardment Wing and had been modified with the refueling area floodlight on the tin tip. The 380th operated a mixed force of KC-135As and KC-135Qs. (380th BMW)

A KC-135A on final passes its strategic stablemate, the Boeing B-52 Stratofortress. Although the two designs are of a similar vintage, the KC-135 continues to be updated and will most likely remain in the inventory far beyond the B-52. (Simon Edwards)

Refueling Area Flood Light

KC-135A (Late)

Extended Fin

KC-135A (Modified)

Refueling Area Flood Light And Fairing

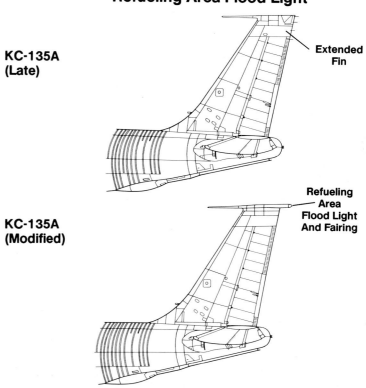

11

A KC-135A (58-0110) on the ramp at K.I. Sawyer Air Force Base. The 410th BMW has exchanged its old vertical Red/White striped tail flash for the new design carried on the fin of this Stratotanker. (410th BMW)

The smoke trail behind this KC-135A Stratotanker (60-0317) lifting off from Wurtsmith AFB, Michigan, was a characteristic of the J57 turbojet. This aircraft is painted overall ADC Gray with a Black radome and anti-glare panel. (379th BMW)

This KC-135A (0-72591) took part in the 1975 "Giant Voice" bombing competition and carried a cartoon of the Wright Flyer and the name Kitty Hawk on the nose in Red. (Larry Davis).

A KC-135A Stratotanker on approach to RAF Fairford. Normally KC-135As deploy to Fairford while KC-135Rs deploy to RAF Mildenhall. Some Fairford based aircraft are sent to Zaragoza AB in Spain and to Riyadh Air Base in Saudi Arabia on a weekly rotational basis, with two aircraft being deployed to each base. (Simon Edwards)

A KC-135A refuels a Republic F-105G Thunderchief of the 561st Tactical Fighter Squadron over Laos during May of 1972. Without tanker support, tactical aircraft would have had difficulty in reaching targets deep in North Vietnam. (Larry Davis)

Trailing the "tell-tale" Black smoke trail, this KC-135A (56-3632) lifts off from RAF Fairford during June of 1988. The aircraft is in overall ADC Gray with Yellow exit markings and a Texas Lone Star flag on the fin. (Simon Edwards)

The small openings beneath the main air intakes on the J57 turbojet engine pods of this KC-135A are cooling air inlets for the oil radiators. The small rectangular opening on the wing leading edge near the fuselage is the housing for a pair of landing/taxi lights. (57th AD)

A KC-135A (56-3632) Stratotanker on final approach for RAF Fairford during 1988. This aircraft was one of the few early KC-135As that was not converted to either an NKC-135A test aircraft or rebuilt as a KC-135E. (Simon Edwards)

A KC-135A refuels a Navy A-6 Intruder using the Flying Boom drogue adapter. The A-6 can take on fuel from the KC-135, then pass this fuel on to other Navy aircraft using the buddy store refueling pod located on the fuselage centerline station. (N.J. Waters III)

A KC-135A equipped with a drogue adapter on the Flying Boom flies formation with a Navy EA-6A Intruder. Through the use of the drogue adapter, KC-135s can refuel Navy aircraft as well as certain Air Force aircraft (such as the A-37) which use the probe and drogue method of refueling. (Larry Davis)

KC-135 Hose & Drouge Adapter

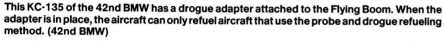

This KC-135 of the 42nd BMW has a drogue adapter attached to the Flying Boom. When the adapter is in place, the aircraft can only refuel aircraft that use the probe and drogue refueling method. (42nd BMW)

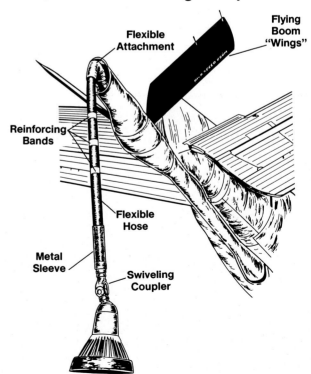

Flexible Attachment

Flying Boom "Wings"

Reinforcing Bands

Flexible Hose

Metal Sleeve

Swiveling Coupler

A camouflaged KC-135A Stratotanker on the ramp at Plattsburg AFB. The post under the tail is to prevent the KC-135 from rocking back on its tail as people move back and fourth within the aircraft. (30th BMW)

Recently the Air Force has allowed the tradition of "nose art" to make a come back. This KC-135A at RAF Fairford during January of 1985 carried a Killer Whale painted on the nose. (Simon Edwards)

A fully camouflaged KC-135A Stratotanker of the 416th Bombardment Wing, Strategic Air Command taxies out for another refueling mission. Most SAC KC-135s are now camouflaged. (Simon Edwards)

This KC-135A has been camouflaged in Dark Gray uppersurfaces over Light Gray undersurfaces. The aircraft has all codes, serials and national markings in Black while emergency markings and exit markings are in Red. (Simon Edwards)

KC-135Q

Externally identical to the KC-135A, the KC-135Q was basically a KC-135A modified with special tanks for JP-7 fuel. These aircraft were used by two squadrons attached to the 9th Strategic Reconnaissance Support Wing at Beale AFB, California and were the dedicated tankers for the SR-71 Blackbird strategic reconnaissance aircraft.

While the KC-135Qs were modified to transfer the Blackbird's exotic JP-7 fuel, they also retained the capability to pass conventional JP-4. Additionally, the aircraft are fitted with a secure communications link for use during SR-71 refueling operations and also carry additional navaids. A total of fifty-six KC-135As were converted to the KC-135Q configuration and two have been lost.

During the Vietnam conflict, KC-135Qs were used to support Blackbird flights out of Kadena AB, Okinawa. The 376th SW on Okinawa operated a number of KC-135Qs, in addition to the unit's standard KC-135As. The 380th BW at Plattsburgh AFB, New York also had a number of KC-135Qs on strength.

A KC-135Q (60-0346) on the taxiway at Plattsburgh AFB. The KC-135Q was externally identical to the KC-1325A although internally it was specially reconfigured to carry JP-7, the primary fuel for the SR-71 Blackbird strategic reconnaissance aircraft. (380th BMW)

The refueling probe makes contact with the refueling receptacle of an SR-71. With the probe in place, a secure communications link between the SR-71 and KC-135Q is established.

This KC-135Q is assigned to the 380th Bombardment Wing. With the retirement of the SR-71, these aircraft will most likely be reconverted to standard tankers or to the KC-135R configuration. (380th BMW)

16

NKC-135A

A number of KC-135As have been used extensively in the test-bed role under the designation NKC-135A.

During the 1960s, a number of Stratotankers were designated as JKC-135As to serve as temporary test-beds. These were later replaced by fourteen KC-135As which were re-designated as NKC-135As for use as permanent test aircraft. A number of these remain in service with the 4950th Test Wing at Wright-Patterson AFB, Ohio and one NKC-135A (55-3119) is operated by the 55th SRW.

The U.S. Navy was given two NKC-135As (55-3134, 56-3596), to equip the Fleet Electronic Warfare Support Group. These aircraft have been given BuNos 553134 and 563596, respectively. The Navy NKC-135As are used for ECM/ECCM training and testing, along with general Electronic Warfare research.

There is no standard configuration for the NKC-135A since each have been put through a number of different modification programs. Some configurations retain the boom, while others have fuel-dump pipes or other alterations in the boom area.

Some of the many programs undertaken by the NKC-135A fleet include: High Energy Laser (HEL) and Airborne Laser Laboratory (55-3123), Winglet testing (55-3129), SLAR testing (55-3132), celestial navigation testing (55-3134), "Big Crow" ICBM vulnerability program (55-3132) and A-LOTS testing (55-3123).

This NKC-135A, on the ramp at NAS Point Mugu, California, was flown by the Fleet Electronic Warfare Support Group for testing various items of Electronic Countermeasures (ECM) equipment. The aircraft is home based at Tulsa, Oklahoma. (Larry Davis)

This NKC-135E (55-3135) was an early production KC-135A that was reconfigured as an NKC-135A testbed. This same aircraft was later re-engined with TF33 turbofan engines. The aircraft was assigned to the 4950th TW. (Simon Edwards)

This NKC-135A testbed was used by NASA to test the upward mounted winglets installed on each wing tip. These winglets increased range and decreased fuel consumption. The nose was also modified with a long pointed test probe. (Via Terry Love)

17

KC-135A Communications Relay — *Combat Lighting*

In order to provide airborne communications relay capability for tactical aircraft conducting combat operations in Southeast Asia, two KC-135As were converted to the communications relay role. These aircraft were modified with numerous small antennas on the upper and lower fuselage and carried an AN/ARC-89 communications relay set internally.

These two aircraft began flying *Combat Lightning* relay missions out of U-Tapao, Thailand, during October of 1966. They were later supplemented by two EC-135Ls, which served until five additional Stratotankers could be converted to the relay configuration. The *Combat Lightning* force was deployed to Ching Chuan Kang AB on Taiwan for a time before returning to U-Tapao.

After the relay aircraft were withdrawn from SEA during 1973, two aircraft were reconfigured back to standard KC-135A configurations. The remaining five have had some of the radio relay equipment removed and operated as standard tankers. These aircraft retain their antennas, internal provisions for the installation of relay gear, J57 power plants and are designated as KC-135A Relay.

A number of tanker KC-135A Relays were used during the late 1970s by a variety of units including: the Pennsylvania Air National Guard, Wisconsin Air National Guard, Utah Air National Guard and Illinois Air National Guard.

A KC-135A Communications Relay aircraft of the 380th BMW based out of Plattsburgh AFB. The KC-135A Relay can be identified by the numerous small blade antennas on the dorsal spine. (Simon Edwards)

KC-135E

The KC-135E is basically a KC-135A modified with uprated engines and new avionics. These aircraft were all part of a modernization program involving some 104 Air National Guard and Air Force Reserve Stratotankers.

The rebuild program involved replacing the original J57 engines with 18,000 lbst JT3D turbofans (removed from 707 airliners purchased by the USAF), the installation of the larger horizontal stabilizers from the 707s, and various avionics improvements.

The JT3D turbofan engines (commercial equivalent of the military TF33) provided a considerable increase in performance (approximately 5,000 lbst per engine) and reliability over the earlier J57 engines. Additionally, engine noise, emissions and fuel consumption have all been reduced. The increased thrust of the JT3D provides a wider safety margin during runway operations and the inclusion of thrust reversers makes it possible for the KC-135E to use shorter runways. The engine also has a cartridge start capability.

The conversion program used already existing parts, providing the ANG and AFRes with a quick and cost-effective way of dealing with the emissions, noise, and performance problems encountered with standard KC-135A operations. The ANG and AFRes operate all KC-135Es, except for two aircraft assigned to SAC. One of these aircraft (59-1514) had been a KC-135R/RC-135R that was reverted to KC-135A status before becoming a KC-135E. This aircraft has a refueling receiver installed and is the only KC-135E with this feature. The first ANG unit to be equipped with the KC-135E was the 197th ARS, Arizona Air National Guard.

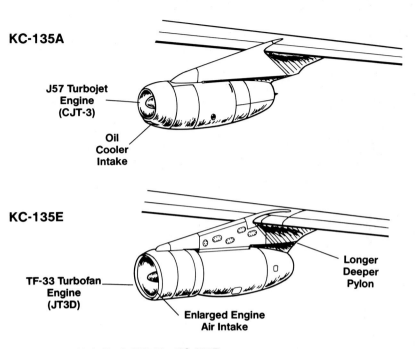

KC-135A

J57 Turbojet Engine (CJT-3)

Oil Cooler Intake

KC-135E

TF-33 Turbofan Engine (JT3D)

Enlarged Engine Air Intake

Longer Deeper Pylon

A KC-135E of the Arkansas Air National Guard on the ramp at Little Rock AFB. The KC-135E was basically a KC-135A with new TF-33 turbofan engines and enlarged horizontal stabilizers. (189th TAG)

The tail band of this overall ADC Gray Maine Air National Guard KC-135E is Green with White bands. The aircraft is assigned to the 132nd ARS based out of Bagor. (Via Terry Love)

This KC-135E has the last four digits of the serial repeated on the nose in White. The aircraft also lacks the refueling area floodlight at the tip of the vertical stabilizer. (Via Terry Love)

A KC-135E (57-2604) of the Wisconsin Air National Guard on final approach to Duluth, Minnesota during August of 1984. All KC-135Es are flown by either Air National Guard or Air Force Reserve units. (Via Terry Love)

A KC-135E (58-0087) of the 150th Air Refueling Squadron, 170th Air Refueling Group, New Jersey Air National Guard. The 150th is based out of McGuire AFB, one of the largest Military Airlift Command bases on the East Coast. (Via Terry Love)

An overall ADC Gray KC-135E of the 197th ARS, 161st ARG, Arizona Air National Guard on the ramp at Fargo during November of 1985. The unit is home based out of Phoenix Airport. (Via Terry Love)

A camouflaged KC-135E of the 108th ARS, 126th Air Refueling Wing, Illinois Air National Guard. This Stratotanker is home based at one of the World's busiest airports, O'Hare Airport, Chicago, Illinois. (Via Terry Love)

The Pennsylvania Air National Guard flies camouflaged KC-135Es. This aircraft is assigned to the 147th ARS, 171st ARW out of Pittsburgh. The tail band is Yellow with a thin Black border. (Via Terry Love)

KC-135R

KC-135Rs are KC-135A airframes that have been put through an extensive rebuilding program carried out at the Boeing Military Airplane Company plant in Wichita, Kansas. The program included the installation of advanced turbofan engines to overcome the KC-135As biggest problem, that of being underpowered.

During the initial phases of the project, the Air Force identified the aircraft to be rebuilt as KC-135REs, possibly to avoid confusion with the KC-135R reconnaissance aircraft (which no longer existed). Several engines were considered including the TF33-P-7 and JT10D, as well as the CFM56 (built by a consortium of General Electric and Snecma of France). The Air Force also considered the possibility of retrofitting 707-320B wings to the KC-135A airframe. In the event, the CFM56 turbofan was ultimately chosen and the wing modification was rejected.

As part of the rebuilding program, the J57 engines are removed and replaced by four 22,000 lbst CFM International CFM56-2B-1 turbofans (military designation F108-CF-100). This type of engine is also used by the E-6 Hermes and export models of the E-3 Sentry. In addition to its far greater thrust (8,250 lbst per engine), the CFM56 burns less fuel, is cleaner and quieter than its turbojet predecessor.

The CFM56 weighs 8,300 pounds, some 2,800 pounds more than the original J57. To handle the additional weight the wing spars were strengthened and the horizontal stabilizers were enlarged to improve longitudinal stability.

The increased power and reduced fuel consumption of the CFM56 radically improves the KC-135Rs performance. The takeoff run is reduced, without the need for water/methanol injection and takeoffs can be made under adverse conditions without reducing the fuel load. The KC-135R has an improved fuel off load capability and under some mission scenarios two KC-135Rs could transfer as much fuel as three KC-135As.

In addition to the new engines, the KC-135R has a number of other improvements. There are two Turbomach T-62T-40LCLL-2 auxiliary power units in the rear of the cabin to provide high-pressure air to the engines. The APUs can be started by lowering the crew access ladder. The increased weight of the KC-135R made it necessary to install strengthened landing gear and MKIII five-rotor anti-skid brakes which replaced the four-rotor brakes of the KC-135A. A high-speed pitch trim system was added for stabilization during refueling of large aircraft. In the cockpit, there are instrumentation changes, some related to the new engines, while others are for the Engine Failure Assist System (EFAS) and other new systems.

On the exterior, a refueling receptacle has been added to the fuselage spine, allowing the KC-135R to take on fuel from other boom-equipped tankers. Additionally, there are two blister windows added to the rear port fuselage.

The first unit to receive the KC-135R was the 384th ARW which accepted its first aircraft during July of 1984. One KC-135R named **Cherokee Rose** set sixteen time-to-climb records on 19 November 1988, and another was used to conduct refueling tests with the Lockheed YF-22 ATF prototype.

A KC-135R (57-1473) on the ramp at Altus AFB, Oklahoma. With its new and improved systems, the KC-135R model is a much safer aircraft to operate than the earlier KC-135A. (443rd MAW)

This KC-135R (62-3533) of the 384th Bomb Wing at McConnell AFB was formerly attached to the 379th Bomb Wing. The tail band consists of Dark Gray and Light Gray diamonds. (384th BW).

A KC-135R of the 11th Air Refueling Squadron, 340th Air Refueling Wing out of Altus AFB, Oklahoma. The tail band consists of Dark Blue and Light Blue diamonds. (Tony Landis)

Engine Development

KC-135A

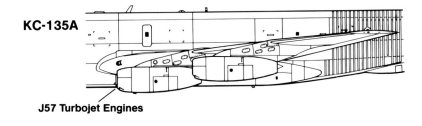

J57 Turbojet Engines

KC-135R

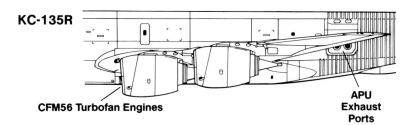

CFM56 Turbofan Engines

APU Exhaust Ports

Eight F-16s of the 363rd Tactical Fighter Wing form up behind a KC-135R to take on fuel during Operation DESERT STORM. KC-135s, along with other tankers, were extensively used during the Gulf War. (USAF)

23

The KC-135R is becoming a familiar visitor to the RAF air fields in the United Kingdom. Thanks to the new engines, the KC-135R's noise level is greatly reduced, which is a great benefit around English airfields. (Simon Edwards)

The KC-135R rebuild/modernization program had extended the useful life of the Stratotanker well into the 21st century. There is no projected replacement for the KC-135 and KC-10 (production of the KC-10 ended with sixty aircraft) and both types are expected to remain in service for the foreseeable future. (Simon Edwards)

A KC-135R of the 42nd Air Refueling Wing, Loring AFB, Maine, refuels an EF-111 Raven of the 366th TFW while his wingman maintains formation on the tanker's port wing. KC-135s were used to support EF-111 operations in both Libya and Iraq. (USAF)

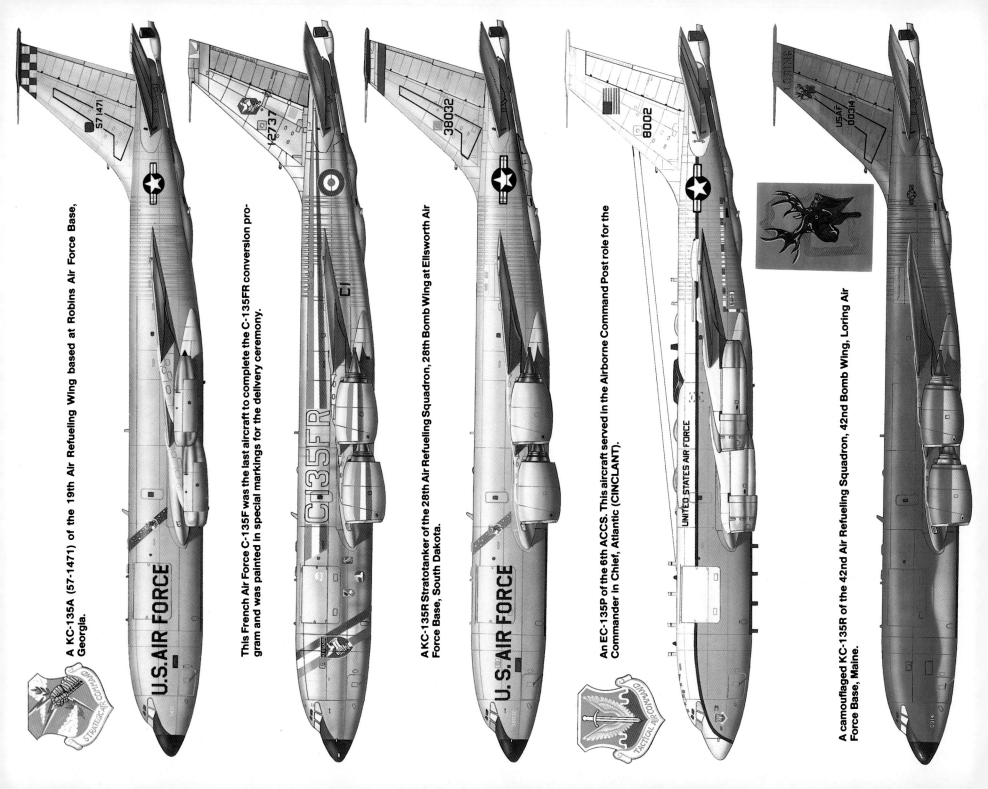

A KC-135A (57-1471) of the 19th Air Refueling Wing based at Robins Air Force Base, Georgia.

This French Air Force C-135F was the last aircraft to complete the C-135FR conversion program and was painted in special markings for the delivery ceremony.

A KC-135R Stratotanker of the 28th Air Refueling Squadron, 28th Bomb Wing at Ellsworth Air Force Base, South Dakota.

An EC-135P of the 6th ACCS. This aircraft served in the Airborne Command Post role for the Commander in Chief, Atlantic (CINCLANT).

A camouflaged KC-135R of the 42nd Air Refueling Squadron, 42nd Bomb Wing, Loring Air Force Base, Maine.

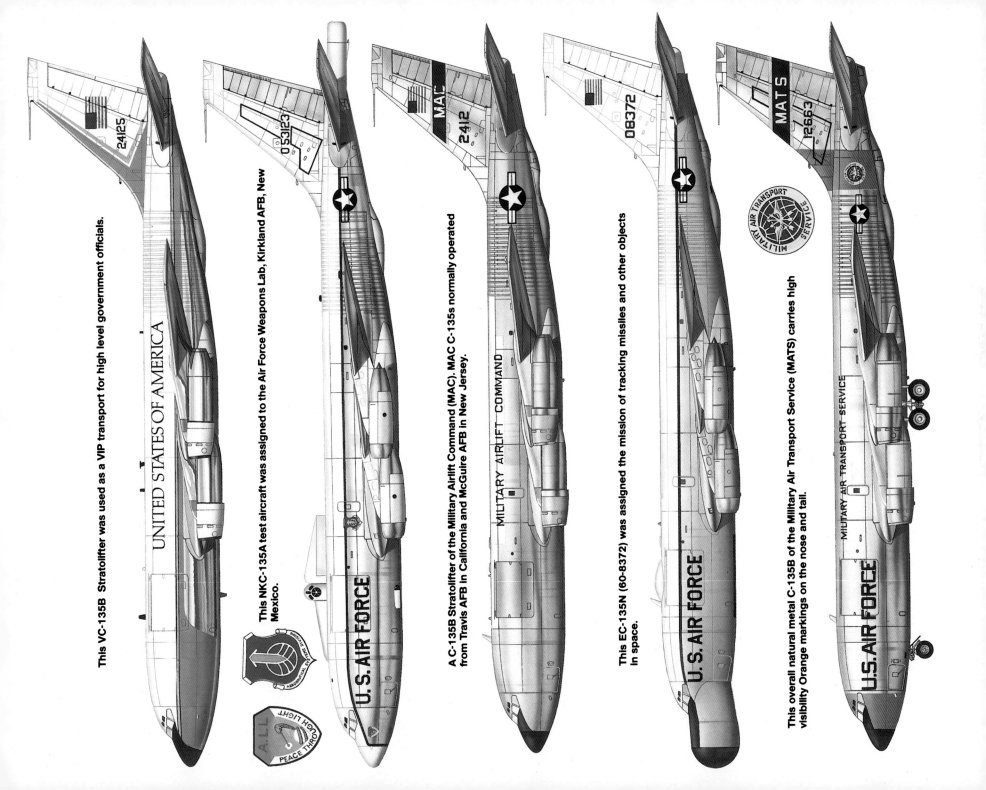

This VC-135B Stratolifter was used as a VIP transport for high level government officials.

UNITED STATES OF AMERICA

24125

This NKC-135A test aircraft was assigned to the Air Force Weapons Lab, Kirkland AFB, New Mexico.

0 53123

U.S. AIR FORCE

PEACE THROUGH LIGHT
A.L.L.

A C-135B Stratolifter of the Military Airlift Command (MAC). MAC C-135s normally operated from Travis AFB in California and McGuire AFB in New Jersey.

MAC
2412

MILITARY AIRLIFT COMMAND

This EC-135N (60-8372) was assigned the mission of tracking missiles and other objects in space.

08372

U.S. AIR FORCE

This overall natural metal C-135B of the Military Air Transport Service (MATS) carries high visibility Orange markings on the nose and tail.

MATS
12663

MILITARY AIR TRANSPORT SERVICE

MILITARY AIR TRANSPORT SERVICE

U.S. AIR FORCE

A KC-135R of the 340th BW on final approach at RAF Fairford, England. The landing gear on the KC-135R was strengthened to handle the increased weight of the upgraded tanker. (Simon Edwards)

A camouflaged KC-135R of the 384th Air Refueling Wing parked and chocked on the ramp at McConnell AFB, Kansas. McConnell AFB is home base for the two squadrons of the 384th ARW, the 91st ARS and 384th ARS. (384th BW)

The two round ports on the fuselage side of this KC-135R (63-7978) of the 70th ARS, 305th ARW are exhaust ports for the auxiliary power unit. The tail band consists of Black squares against the aircraft's camouflage (originally the band was Black and White squares). (Simon Edwards)

The large cargo door in the fuselage side of the KC-135R gives the aircraft a cargo capacity, although the KC-135R is not primarily an airlift aircraft. (443rd MAW)

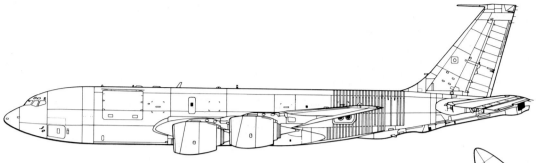

Specifications

Boeing KC-135R Stratotanker

Wingspan .130 feet 10 inches
Length . . . . .136 feet 3 inches
Height . . . . .41 feet 8 inches
Maximum Weight . . . . .322,500 pounds
Powerplant . . . . .Four 22,000 lbst CFM
International CFM56-2B-1
trubofan engines.

Armament . . . . .None

Performance
  Maximum Speed . . . . .610 mph
  Service ceiling . . . . .45,000 feet
  Range . . . . .11,309 miles
Crew . . . . .Four

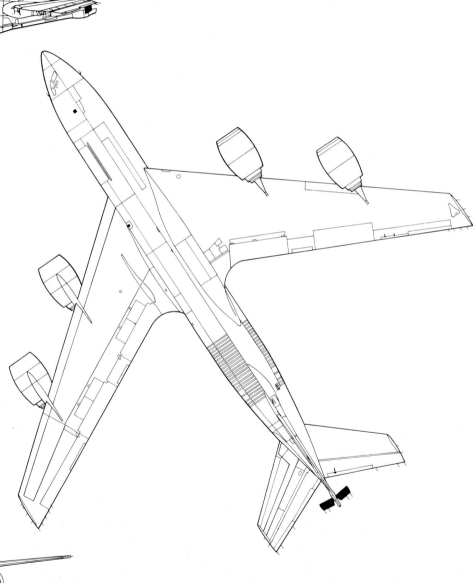

A KC-135R of the 905th Air Refueling Squadron, 319th Bomb Wing on the ramp at Grand Forks Air Force Base, North Dakota during October of 1989. The 319th BW is under the operational control of the 15th Air Force. (Via Terry Love)

This KC-135R Stratotanker of the 28th ARS, 28th Bomb Wing carried the name *HOOVER* on the nose in Light Gray during May of 1990. (Via Terry Love)

This KC-135R is assigned to the 28th Air Refueling Squadron, 28th Bomb Wing, 15th Air Force and is based at Ellsworth Air Force Base, South Dakota. As with the earlier ADC Gray paint scheme, the engine pod intake lip on this camouflaged KC-135R, is in polished natural metal. (Via Terry Love)

Transports

C-135A

During the early 1960s, the Air Force identified a need for an interim high speed, long range transport for the Military Air Transport Service (MATS), to provide fast logistical airlift until the Lockheed C-141 Starlifter became available. Utilizing the inherent transport capabilities of the KC-135A, Boeing converted three Stratotankers to the transport configuration during 1961 under the designation C-135A. These aircraft were modified with the refueling boom deleted, but retained the boom operator's pod.

These initial conversions were followed by fifteen production C-135A Stratolifters (Boeing Model 717-157). These aircraft featured the higher fin and powered rudder of the later KC-135A and were powered by J57 engines. The bulk of the C-135A force went to McGuire AFB, New Jersey.

Replaced on the production line by the C-135B, the C-135A was to be the basis for several special purpose conversions. Two aircraft still serve as C-135As, one with the 4950th TW, the other with the 55th SRW.

C-135B

First flown on 15 February 1962, the C-135B was the definitive transport variant of the Stratotanker/Stratolifter family. Designated by Boeing as the Model 717-158, the C-135B was powered by four Pratt & Whitney TF33-PW-5 turbofans replacing the earlier J57 turbojets of previous models. Like the earlier C-135A, these aircraft had the refueling boom deleted but retained the operator's pod.

Deliveries of C-135Bs to MATS was completed by August of 1962. Thirty aircraft were produced, equipping the 1611th ATW at McGuire AFB, New Jersey, and the 1501st ATW at Travis AFB, California. Although soon superseded by the C-141, the C-135B Stratolifters had active transport careers. Missions flown by C-135Bs included airlifting arms to India, and supplying TAC and the Guantanamo Naval Base in Cuba during the Cuban Missile Crisis of October 1962. One C-135B (62-4136) was lost in an accident during the Guantanamo operation.

After replacement in MATS/MAC service, the majority of C-135Bs were modified for reconnaissance and electronics missions, although five still serve as VIP transports.

C-135C

Three WC-135Bs were reconverted to the transport role under the designation C-135C. These aircraft retain the air refueling capability and are the only C-135 transports to have this feature. Two C-135Cs are used by Detachment One of the 89th MAW, while 61-2669 is operated by Detachment One of the 4950th Test Wing. 61-2669 has been used in the avionics testing role.

VC-135B

The VC-135B is a Special Air Mission VIP transport conversion. Five C-135Bs were given VIP interiors and assigned to the 89th MAW. Most were used as staff transports for high level officials.

A C-135A (60-0377) of the 44th Air Transport Squadron, 1501st Air Transport Wing, Military Air Transport Service over San Francisco Bay. MATS C-135A flew out of Travis Air Force Base located near San Francisco. (USAF)

Tail Development

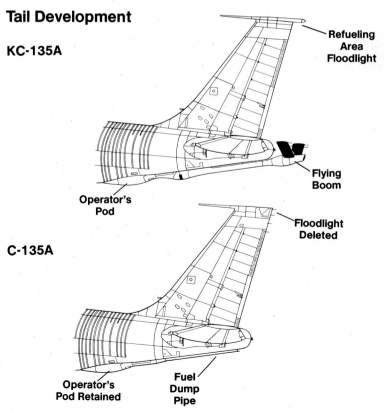

KC-135A

Refueling Area Floodlight

Flying Boom

Operator's Pod

C-135A

Floodlight Deleted

Operator's Pod Retained

Fuel Dump Pipe

A C-135B Stratolifter (61-2663) of the Military Air Transport Service (MATS). This aircraft was later converted to the RC-135S reconnaissance configuration. The aircraft carried Red-Orange bands on the nose, rear fuselage and wing tips. (Boeing)

The C-135B Stratolifter was basically a KC-135 airframe equipped with turbofan engines and modified for the transport role. Although the Flying Boom of the KC-135A was deleted, the boom pod was retained to ease production. (Boeing)

A C-135C staff transport shares the ramp at RAF Fairford, England with a camouflaged KC-135A during April of 1988. C-135Cs are used to ferry high-level Air Force and government officials. (Simon Edwards)

Reconnaissance Variants

The Stratotanker/Stratolifter family has served as the basis for a large number of strategic reconnaissance aircraft which have played significant roles in USAF intelligence gathering operations for over twenty years.

RC-135s are primarily used for peripheral intelligence missions around the borders of the USSR and other potential aggressor nations, flying stand-off collection missions. RC-135s have been used for Electronic Intelligence (ELINT), Side-Looking Airborne Radar (SLAR) reconnaissance and visual inspection of reentry vehicles from Soviet ballistic missile tests.

Active measures such as jamming and the transmitting of spurious communications can also play a part in RC-135 missions. These measures can be used to force a target to turn on dormant transmitters or to shift to alternate frequencies. These actions can then be recorded by passive listening gear.

Because of the large size of the KC-135/C-135, large amounts of interior equipment can be installed, changed or removed easily through the fuselage cargo door. Much of the internal electronic equipment is carried forward in the cabin, while the operator positions are in the rear fuselage. RC-135s can differ internally from others of the same model, as reconfigurations can easily be made for specific mission requirements.

All RC-135 assets come under the control of two SAC wings: the 55th SRW at Offutt AFB, Nebraska, and the 6th SW based at Eielson AFB, Alaska. In order to maintain complete coverage of target areas, there are several forward bases for the use of the RC-135 fleet. These include: RAF Mildenhall in the United Kingdom, Hellenikon AB in Greece, and Kadena AB on Okinawa.

All current RC-135s are conversions of C-135B transports or earlier RC-135Bs. The fuel-efficient TF33-P-5/9-9 turbofan power plants on these aircraft, along with the addition of refueling receivers, give the RC-135s greatly extended endurance (relief crews are carried). Antenna installations are extensive and varied. Many different types of aerials, fairings and radomes can be seen on RC-135s. One common modification is an extended thimble shaped nose radome, known as the *Hognose*, which encloses a larger nose radar.

RC-135s were active during the Vietnam War, U.S. military actions against Libya during 1986 and Operation DESERT STORM. No RC-135 has been lost to hostile action, despite the fact that fighters from target nations often shadow the aircraft during missions. The Korean Airlines 747 airliner shot down over the Sea of Japan by Soviet fighters on 1 September 1983 may have been mistaken for an RC-135 by Soviet air defense forces (an RC-135S had been airborne in the area on that day).

KC-135R/RC-135R

Not to be confused with the much later KC-135R re-engined tanker, the initial KC-135R model was the first KC-135 aircraft to be configured for reconnaissance duties. The fourth KC-135A (55-3121) was modified with an ELINT capsule that was reeled out from the aircraft in flight. It eventually received five rows of fence aerials on the upper fuselage. Operated by the 55th SRW, 55-3121 was known to have been used with the CIA's *Briar Patch* and *Iron Lung* programs. Four more KC-135As were later modified to KC-135R standard.

Some features seen on later RC-135s, such as the *Hognose* radome and the rear fuselage teardrop radome, were first installed on KC-135Rs. Two aircraft had photographic capability, with camera bays in the fuselage cargo doors. The KC-135R was unique in that it was the only recon version to retain the Flying Boom.

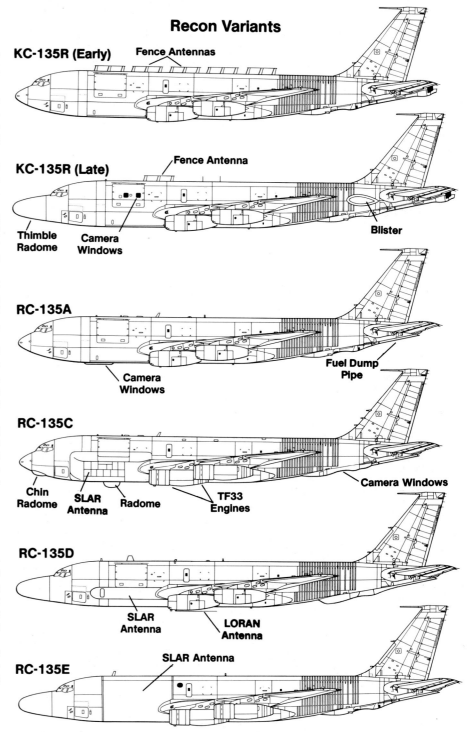

Recon Variants

KC-135R (Early) — Fence Antennas

KC-135R (Late) — Fence Antenna — Blister — Thimble Radome — Camera Windows

RC-135A — Camera Windows — Fuel Dump Pipe

RC-135C — Chin Radome — SLAR Antenna — Radome — TF33 Engines — Camera Windows

RC-135D — SLAR Antenna — LORAN Antenna

RC-135E — SLAR Antenna

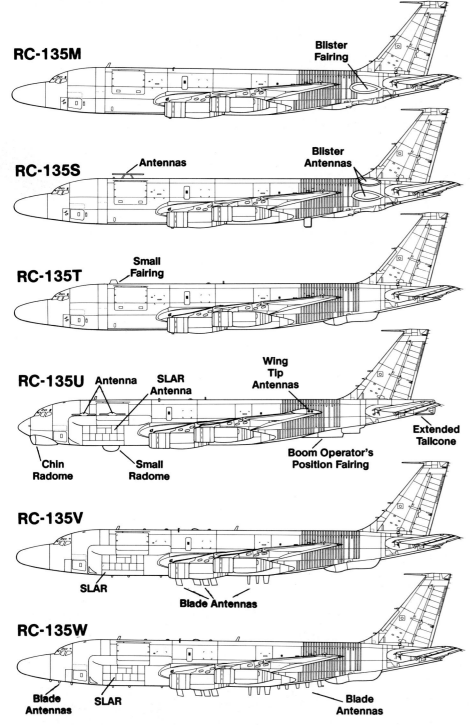

RC-135M
Blister Fairing

RC-135S
Antennas
Blister Antennas

RC-135T
Small Fairing

RC-135U
Antenna
SLAR Antenna
Wing Tip Antennas
Extended Tailcone
Boom Operator's Position Fairing
Chin Radome
Small Radome

RC-135V
SLAR
Blade Antennas

RC-135W
Blade Antennas
SLAR
Blade Antennas

With the advent of more sophisticated RC-135s, the KC-135Rs (or RC-135Rs, as they were later designated) were phased out of service. 55-3121 became the RC-135T before its loss during 1985 and three other survivors were reconverted back to KC-135As, with at least one being re-engined as a KC-135E. One aircraft (59-1465) was lost during 1967.

RC-135A

Among the last C-135s built (and the last to be delivered) were four aircraft modified for photographic reconnaissance under the designation RC-135As (Boeing Model 739-445). Camera bays were installed in the underside of the forward fuselage and the RC-135As were originally used by MATS/MAC for photographic and geodetic surveying work out of Turner AFB, Georgia. It was planned to procure an additional five RC-135As, but these were cancelled. The entire force was turned over to SAC and assigned to the 55th SRW during 1972, which used them as support aircraft. Later, during the late 1970s, the entire group was converted to the tanker configuration under the designation KC-135D.

RC-135B

The RC-135B was the ELINT version of the KC-135/C-135. Powered by TF33-PW-9 turbofans engines, a total of ten were produced with the Boeing designation Model 739-445Bs during 1964-65. These were to be the last examples of the Stratotanker/Stratolifter family off the production line, all others being modifications of existing airframes. The RC-135B was the basis for numerous ELINT conversions.

This KC-135R/RC-135R of the 82nd SRS, 4252nd SRW, was formerly a KC-135A tanker before it was converted to the reconnaissance role. The KC-135R has a thimble nose radome and a three blade fence antenna above the fuselage. (via Terry Love)

RC-135C

Shortly after the RC-135B entered service it was the subject of a modification program which resulted in the redesignation of the aircraft as RC-135Cs. The modification entailed the installation of additional equipment and antennas, as well as Side Looking Airborne Radar (SLAR). The SLAR installation consisted of prominent "cheeks" on both sides of the forward fuselage to house the SLAR antennas. The aircraft also were configured with a KA-59 camera mounted in a bay on the boom pod. These same airframes were to undergo further modifications: three being converted to the RC-135U configuration, while the remainder became RC-135Vs.

RC-135D *Rivet Brass*

One KC-135A and three C-135As (KC-135A transport conversions) became RC-135Ds during 1962-63. As part of the conversion, a SLAR antenna was fitted in cylinder-shaped fairings on both sides of the forward fuselage, beginning at the wing roots (a similar SLAR configuration was tested on NKC-135A [55-3132]). The RC-135Ds were also modified with *Hognose* radomes and had fence aerials above the fuselage.

Compared to other RC-135 models, the RC-135D had a shorter range, due to the retention of the KC-135A J57 turbojet power plants. RC-135Ds participated in the Vietnam conflict, occasionally flying *Combat Apple* missions. One RC-135D (59-1491) was converted to an RC-135S and the surviving RC-135Ds were later reconverted back to KC-135A tankers.

RC-135E *Rivet Amber*

One of the most unusual RC-135 variants, the RC-135E was a conversion of a C-135B (62-4137) which had a major portion of the forward fuselage structure removed and replaced by a unique fiberglass radome which housed a Hughes SLAR antenna. Cameras were installed to allow photography of missile reentry vehicles and ELINT pods were mounted under the wings. Used by the 6th SW, the *Lisa Ann*, as the RC-135E was codenamed, was lost during a 1969 flight over the Bering Strait. The cause of the crash was believed to be due to the failure of the radome structure.

RC-135M *Rivet Card/Rivet Quick*

Six RC-135Bs were converted during 1967-68, receiving *Hognose* radomes and teardrop-shaped rear fuselage fairings as part of an (at least externally) austere modification program under the designation RC-135M. Additionally, antenna arrays were installed in the faired-over boom position.

Originally assigned to the 4252nd SRW, the RC-135Ms saw extensive use during the Vietnam War, flying *Combat Apple* ELINT missions out of Kadena AB, Okinawa. The RC-135Ms were later used by the 55th SRW, flying out of RAF Mildenhall. These airframes were the subject of an extensive rebuild program during the early 1980s, being redesignated as RC-135Ws.

RC-135S *Rivet Ball/Cobra Ball*

Used by the 6th SW, the first RC-135S was a conversion of a KC-135A (59-1491) to the Telemetry Intelligence (TELINT) role. The RC-135S was used to gather information on Soviet missile tests. The first RC-135S was lost during January of 1969 being replaced by two converted C-135Bs and one C-135B T/RIA. A second RC-135S (61-2664) was lost during 1981 and one other KC-135A may have been partially converted before it was lost during 1968.

The RC-135S series has featured a number of different configurations, all of which

This RC-135M (62-4138) of the 55th SRW was undergoing an engine inspection during July of 1979. The RC-135M has a thimble nose radome and electronics blisters on either side of the rear fuselage. (Via Terry Love)

This RC-135U of the 55th SRW has wing mounted HF probe antennas, a chin antenna fairing, SLAR cheek antenna fairings on each side of the fuselage and two large antenna arrays mounted above each SLAR fairing. (Via Terry Love)

featured the elongataed *Hognose* radome. More recently, cameras have been installed and the surviving aircraft are used to fly missions code named *Burning Star*.

RC-135U/*Combat Sent/Combat Pink*

Three RC-135Cs became RC-135Us during 1971. Initially, the RC-135U conversion was minor, consisting of an extended tailcone and the installation of an electronics fairing on the vertical fin above the rudder.

RC-135Us were later modified with a number of new features, becoming the most radically modified type of RC-135 presently in service. A chin radome was added behind and below the standard nose radome, a second radome was added below the forward fuselage, two *Rabbit Ear* antennas were mounted above each SLAR installation and the boom position was faired over (in a more angular fashion than with similar installations on other RC-135s).

The RC-135Us flew *Combat Sent* missions during the later stages of the Vietnam War. One aircraft (64-14848) was reconfigured during 1977 becoming redesignated as an RC-135V during 1977. The remaining aircraft were still on active service during 1991.

RC-135V

A modification of seven RC-135C airframes and one RC-135U (64-14848), the RC-135V is currently the most numerous RC-135 variant in service. The RC-135V was the first variant to incorporate both SLAR cheek antenna fairings and the *Hognose* radome. Additionally, there are four large blade antennas mounted under the center section of the fuselage with another three blade antennas mounted further back under the fuselage. A retrofit has recently introduced even more ventral antennas, similar to the RC-135W configuration. At present, the RC-135Vs operate in the Mediterranean and Middle East regions flying out of Hellenikon AB, Greece.

RC-135W (62-4134) on the ramp at RAF Fairford, England during October of 1985. Originally built as the twenty-fifth C-135B, this aircraft of the 55th SRW was first converted to the RC-135M configuration before being re-converted to the RC-135W configuration. (Simon Edwards)

RC-135W

All six of the RC-135Ms underwent a rebuilding program during the early 1980s being redesignated as RC-135W. These aircraft are equipped to a standard close to that of the RC-135V, although they have additional under fuselage antennas.

RC-135X/*Cobra Eye*

One C-135B (62-4128) was rebuilt and redesignated as the RC-135X *Cobra Eye*. This aircraft is associated with the Optical Aircraft Measurements Program and was currently still in flight testing. The aircraft was intended to gather imagery of Soviet missile tests for the SDI "Star War" program.

Recon Training Variants

Because the aerodynamic configurations of the various RC-135s differ from those of standard KC/C-135s, there were two reconnaissance trainer conversions of KC-135 airframes.

RC-135T

Late in its career, a KC-135R/RC-135R (55-3121) was phased into the training role shortly after it was retrofitted with TF33 turbofan engines. Unfortunately, 55-3121 was lost in Alaska during February of 1985.

TC-135S

To replace the lost RC-135T, an EC-135B (62-4133) was converted to the training role as the TC-135S. The aircraft is assigned to the 6th SW.

An RC-135W on the ramp at RAF Fairford during October of 1988. This aircraft has slightly larger SLAR antenna fairings than on the similar RC-135V. The port side fairing protrudes into the crew access hatch. (Simon Edwards)

An RC-135V (64-14845) of the 55th SRW on final approach to landing. The RC-135V has numerous blade antennas mounted under the fuselage. As with most other RC-135 variants, the RC-135V began life as an RC-135B. (Via Terry Love)

The RC-135U is an unusual configuration with a normal nose radome, chin fairing, SLAR antennas and two large antennas mounted above the SLAR fairings. These antennas are known as "Rabbit Ears." (Via Terry Love)

This RC-135V on the ramp at Offutt AFB has a ground support power cart plugged in to provide the aircraft with electrical power while the engines are shut down. The thimble nose radome of the RC-135 series makes these aircraft very distinctive. (Via Terry Love)

An RC-135V (62-4139) on the ramp at SAC Headquarters, Offutt Air Force Base. The RC-135V has numerous large blade antennas on the fuselage underside. (Via Terry Love)

An RC-135W (64-14841) of the 55th Strategic Reconnaissance Wing. The engine pylons have small air intakes in the front of each pylon that supply air to the air conditioners needed to keep the electronics cool. (Via Terry Love)

An RC-135V (63-9792) of the 55th SRW on final approach for landing. RC-135Vs saw action during Operation DESERT STORM, providing near real time intelligence information on Iraqi defenses. (Via Terry Love)

Electronics Variants

Because virtually all U.S. land-based military command and communication facilities would probably be destroyed in the opening stages of a nuclear conflict, the USAF operates the Post Attack Command Control System (PACCS), an airborne command and communications system that mainly uses KC-135/C-135 derivatives which have the capability to take over command and control from destroyed ground installations.

The command function of this system is carried out by various types of Airborne Command Post aircraft. The most numerous of the ABCPs are thirteen SAC EC-135C Airborne National Command Posts, one of which, until 1990, was airborne at all times. Designed to take over from SAC Headquarters at Omaha, Nebraska, the ABNCPs can order U.S. nuclear forces into action under orders from the President airborne in an E-4B. In addition to the ABNCPs, there are several "theater" ABCP versions for use by the various Commanders in Chiefs including: CINCPAC, CINCLANT, CINCENT, CINC-SOUTH, etc.

Tying together the various ABCPs and any surviving ground stations in wartime would be the job of a fleet of radio relay aircraft, all of these being conversions of KC-135As. One of these relay types, the EC-135G, also serves as an Airborne Launch Control Center (ALCC), able to launch SAC ICBMs if ground control centers are disabled.

As would be expected, the EC-135 ABCP and relay variants are well equipped for communications, with a large numbers of antennas. To boost endurance, all have refueling receivers on the upper fuselage. These allow flights of up to 72 hours duration, the limiting factor being engine oil supplies. Virtually all still have the Flying Boom fitted and, at least some aircraft can use the boom in reverse, to draw off fuel from receivers. This capability would be invaluable if tankers were not available, as well might be the case in wartime. Most of the early J57-powered variants have been re-engined with the more fuel efficient and powerful JT3D/TF33 turbofan engines.

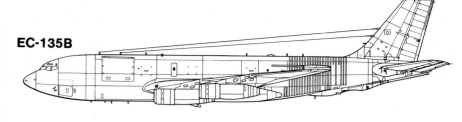

EC-135B

EC-135A

The first Stratotanker relay derivatives for PACCS were six conversions of KC-135As designated as EC-135As during 1965. These aircraft were given an aerial refueling capability and extra antennas, but retained the J57 engines. One aircraft was reverted to the KC-135A configuration before being converted to the initial KC-135R. Five aircraft remain in service.

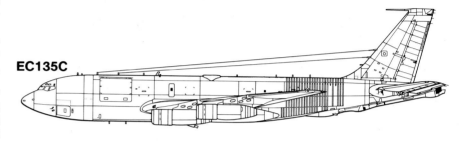

EC135C

EC-135B

Two of the C-135B T/RIAs were put to use in the ARIA role during 1978-79, as EC-135Bs. Of these two, 62-4133 later became the TC-135S, while 62-4128 became the RC-135X.

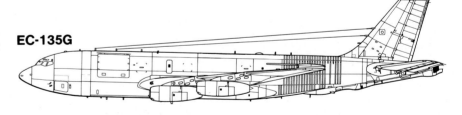

EC-135G

EC-135C

The most well known of the KC/C-135 ABCP variants, the EC-135Cs were originally part of an order for seventeen KC-135Bs. The aircraft were powered by TF33-P-9 turbofan engines and equipped as tankers. These aircraft were equipped with elaborate communications gear to allow them to function as ABCPS for SAC, replacing KC-135As originally used in that role.

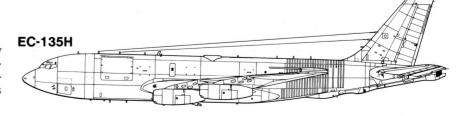

EC-135H

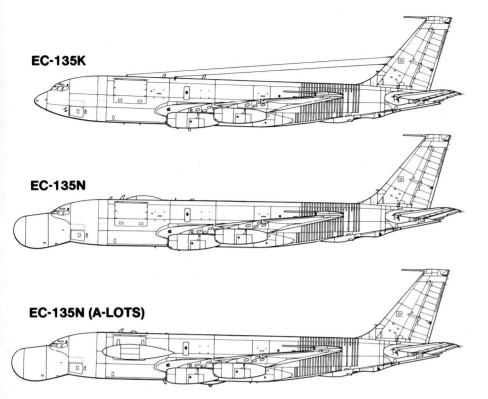

EC-135K

EC-135N

EC-135N (A-LOTS)

EC-135H

The EC-135Hs are conversions of five KC-135As with a dorsal "saddle" antenna on the fuselage spine and numerous blade antennas. One example (61-0274) is used for CINCLANT by the 6th ACCS, while the remainder fly out of RAF Mildenhall under the control of the 10th ACCS.

EC-135K

Two KC-135As, including the first production aircraft (55-3118, City of Renton) were converted to serve as Tactical Air Command airborne command posts under the designation EC-135K. EC-135Ks accompany TAC aircraft on long deployments to provide communication links and accurate navigational data. Refueling cannot be done with the EC-135K, since the type has a fuel-dump pipe rather than a refueling boom. The aircraft are assigned to the 8th TDCS of the 552nd AW & CW at Tinker AFB, Oklahoma. EC-135K 62-3536 was lost during 1977 and was replaced by a conversion of KC-135A 59-1518. These aircraft have been re-engined with TF33 turbofans.

EC-135L

Eight KC-135As were converted to radio relay aircraft during 1965 under the designation EC-135L. Used as communications relay aircraft, the EC-135Ls have blade antennas above and below the fuselage. The modification of the aircraft was kept simple and the KC-135L retains the original J57 power plants of the KC-135A. Five aircraft remain in service with the 305th ARW.

Upon delivery to SAC during the mid-1960s, fourteen of the KC-135Bs were redesignated as EC-135Cs, retaining the SAC command post mission, while the remaining three were redesignated as EC-135J ABCPs for the National Command Authority.

These aircraft carry a dorsal "saddle" antenna along with various blade and dipole antennas, HF probes and a VLF trailing wire antenna. The EC-135C fleet has received updates in recent years and are now equipped with AFSATCOM UHF communications equipment and improved computer and display capabilities.

Until 1990, at least one EC-135C was airborne at all times, flying eight-hour missions that did not end until another EC-135C was airborne and ready to take over. Currently, the KC-135Cs stand runway alert with an officer of general rank aboard as the Airborne Emergency Actions Officer.

Nine EC-135Cs are on strength with the 2nd ACCS, 55th SRW while the other four are attached to the 4th ACCS of the 28th Bomb Wing.

EC-135G

Aside from the EC-135A and EC-135L, PACCS also uses four EC-135Gs in the relay role. These aircraft, in addition to their relay capability, can remotely launch Minuteman ICBMs while airborne. All four aircraft are conversions of KC-135A airframes equipped with Aerial Refueling Receptacles (ARRs) and are assigned to the 4th ACCS.

This aircraft was the ninth EC-135C (63-8049) built. Like many other special purpose KC-135 variants, the SAC fuselage sash does not completely encircle the fuselage. (USAF)

EC-135P

There are five ex-KC-135As modified as Airborne Command Posts under the designation EC-135P. These aircraft were initially used to support CINCPAC, but are now operated for CINCLANT by the 6th ACCS, based at Langley AFB, Virginia. One aircraft was lost and two (58-0011, 58-0018) have been reconverted to the tanker configuration. The two survivors have been re-engined with TF33 turbofans.

EC-135Y

The EC-135Y was a conversion of an NKC-135A (55-3125) for use as an Airborne Command Post by CINCENT (Central Command) during 1984. The aircraft is assigned to the 19th ARW.

EC-135N

To support the Apollo lunar-landing program, eight C-135As were modified by Douglas during 1967 as Apollo Range Instrumentation Aircraft. The former transports were given large nose radomes that contain an eighty-five inch steerable dish antenna and four were modified with the Northrop A-LOTS (Airborne Lightweight Optical Tracking System), first tested on NKC-135A (55-3123). The A-LOTS was housed in a pod mounted forward on the port side of the fuselage.

Operated by the 6549th Test Squadron at Patrick AFB, the EC-135Ns provided tracking and communications relay capability during the Apollo flights. After the Apollo program ended, the EC-135Ns were redesignated Advanced Range Instrumentation Aircraft (ARIA). The EC-135N ARIAs were later redesignated as C-135Ns and assigned to special test programs.

EC-135E

This designation refers to EC-135Ns that were re-engined with TF33-PW-102 engines. Replaced in the ARIA role by the EC-18B (707 conversions), the aircraft are now used as testbeds by the 4950th TW.

C-135B T/RIA

Four C-135Bs were converted to T/RIA (Telemetry/Range Instrumentation Aircraft) configuration with the same nose radome as the EC-135N under the designation C-135B T/RIA. One was lost, one became a RC-135S and two were converted to the EC-135B configuration.

Weather Reconnaissance

WC-135B

During 1965, ten C-135B turbofan engined transports were converted to WC-135B weather reconnaissance platforms. The WC-135Bs are well equipped for weather reconnaissance and are also fitted for atmospheric particle sampling with collection foils mounted on each side of the fuselage. To increase endurance, the aircraft were modified with the addition of refueling receivers.

Six aircraft remain in the weather reconnaissance role with the 55th WRS at McClellan AFB. Of the other four, one is now a trainer for the 552nd AW & CW, and three have been modified as transports under the designation C-135C. Two C-135Cs are assigned to Det 1, 89th MAW, while the third aircraft is assigned to Det 1, 4950th Test Wing.

This EC-135C (62-3585) is flown by the 2nd ACCS, 55th SRW, out of Offutt AFB. At least one EC-135 is normally on runway alert. (Via Terry Love)

An EC-135C (62-3585) of the 55th SRW on the ramp at Offutt AFB during July of 1979. The EC-135C is the most numerous EC-135 variant with at least thirteen aircraft still in service. (Via Terry Love)

An EC-135H *Silk Purse* based at RAF Mildenhall, England. Four EC-135Hs are assigned to Mildenhall as Airborne Command Posts for the U.S. Commander in Chief Europe (CINCEUR). They have been updated with TF33 turbofan engines. The blisters in front of and behind the saddle antenna are part of a satellite navigation system. (Simon Edwards)

An overall high gloss White EC-135K (59-1518) of the 8th TDCS on the ramp at RAF Fairford during September of 1988. At one point in its career this aircraft was used by the FAA. (Simon Edwards)

This EC-135K was the first production KC-135A. The aircraft was reconfigured with TF33 turbofan engines and outfitted as an Airborne Command Post. The aircraft was based at Tinker AFB. (28th AD/USAF)

The Very Low Frequency (VLF) Trailing Antenna is carried in a housing faired into the fuselage underside. The basket on the end of the antenna helps keep the wire stretched out when deployed. (Via Terry Love)

An EC-135J (63-8055) on the ramp at Hickam AFB, Hawaii. Externally the EC-135J is very similar to the earlier EC-135C, except for the three blisters on the upper fuselage for the new navigation system. (15th ABW)

An EC-135N of the Aeronautical Systems Division, 4950th Test Wing, Air Force Systems Command. These aircraft carry special antennas to track space vehicles. (Via Terry Love)

The nose radome on the EC-135N houses an eighty-five inch steerable antenna. These aircraft were first used to support the Apollo program but have since been modified as Advanced Range Instrumentation Aircraft (ARIA). (via Terry Love)

Some EC-135Ns have been redesignated as C-135Ns and assigned to special test programs. This aircraft is assigned to ASD, the Aeronautical Systems Division of Air Force Systems Command. (Via Terry Love)

This EC-135P (58-0022) of the 6th ACCS operated out of Langley Air Force Base, Virginia. The aircraft has a saddle antenna and wing mount HF antenna probes. This aircraft was later retrofitted with TF33 engines.(HQ TAC)

This WC-135B was the seventh C-135B (61-2666) Stratolifter produced. The aircraft was later converted to become the second WC-135B weather reconnaissance aircraft. (55th WRS)

WC-135Bs are all conversions of C-135B transports. They have air sampling intakes mounted on each side of the fuselage and are powered by TF33 turbofan engines. (55th WRS)

WC-135Bs are flown by the 55th Weather Reconnaissance Squadron, Military Airlift Command based at McClellan AFB, California. The tail band is Blue with White stars. (Mark Gray)

Exports

C-135F

As successful an aircraft as the KC-135 has been, the only foreign air arm to operate the type has been the French *Armee de l' Air*. The French began establishing their own strategic nuclear force during the 1960s and equipped the bomber portion of this arm with the Dassault Mirage IVA. Since the Mirage IVA had a limited range, in-flight refueling was necessary for the aircraft to pose an effective threat against targets in the USSR. As a result, twelve C-135Fs were ordered from Boeing during 1962, to serve as tankers for the Mirage force.

Similar to the KC-135, the C-135F was equipped with the Flying Boom, but had the probe-and-drogue adapter permanently fitted, since France uses that system for refueling. The C-135F carries no "K" prefix in the designation, since the French stressed the aircraft's dual tanker/transport role . All C-135Fs were delivered with standard J57 turbojet engines.

Deliveries of C-135Fs began during February of 1964 and were completed by July of 1965. At first, the C-135F units, *Escadrilles*, were grouped together under the control of one wing, the 90th *Escadre de Ravitaillement en Vol*, at Istres. Later, this unit was disbanded and the C-135F squadrons were dispersed, one to each of the Mirage IVA units.

In addition to supporting France's strategic bomber force, the C-135Fs have also refueled tactical aircraft and transported men and material to locations worldwide and one C-135F (63-473), was lost in the South Pacific on 30 June 1972.

Following the retirement of some Mirage IVA bombers during 1976, the C-135F units were brought together within the 93rd *Escadre*, a former Mirage IVA unit. *Escadrilles* presently operating the type are as follows: ERV 1/93 at Istres, ERV 2/93 at Avord, and ERV 3/93 at Mont-de-Marsan.

During 1978-79, the C-135Fs were put through the ECP 405 lower wing skin replacement program carried out by Boeing at Wichita. During 1981, it was decided to refit the entire force with CFM56/F-108 turbofan engines. Again the modification program was undertaken at Wichita, with the first re-engined C-135FR being delivered to the *Armee de l' Air* during August of 1985.

In an effort to reduce the visibility of the big Boeings, they have been given a Blue-Gray camouflage paint scheme with reduced sized fuselage roundels.

A French Air Force C-135F tanker. The French tankers usually flew with the drogue adapter fitted to the boom at all times, since French tactical aircraft employ the hose and drogue method of refueling.

A Mirage IVP bomber moves into position to take on fuel from a camouflaged French C-135FR Stratotanker (93-CA). The Mirage carries an ASMP stand off missile on the centerline station. (SIRPA/AIR via Antoine J. Givuadon)

A French Air Force C-135FR refuels a Dassualt-Breguet Mirage F1 fighter. The C-135FR is the designation given to French C-135F aircraft that were re-engined with turbofan engines. (SIRPA/AIR via Antonie J. Givaudon)

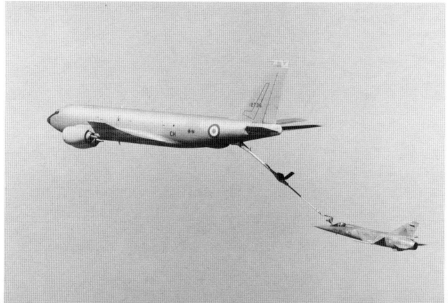

A C-135FR refuels a Mirage IVA bomber. The French Stratotanker force, although small when compared to the USAF, is nonetheless a potent force multiplier for the French air force. (SIRPA/AIR via Antoine J. Givaudon)

Combat

Although not a "combat" aircraft in the strictest sense of the word, KC-135s have been involved in a number of crisis situations, "surgical" military actions, and "limited" wars.

During the Cuban Missile Crisis of October 1962, SAC placed a portion of its tanker force on airborne alert. KC-135s stood ready to refuel B-47s, B-52s and B-58s if the order to strike came through. No such order was issued; however, C-135 Stratolifters were used to supply the U.S. naval base in Cuba with the material necessary for operations on a day-to-day basis.

MATS used ten C-135Bs for a rapid airlift of badly needed light armaments and ammunition to India during November of 1963, following border clashes between India and the People's Republic of China. Ten C-135Bs flew shuttle flights from Rhein-Main Air Base in Germany to Adana, Turkey, then on to Calcutta. Two C-135As were also involved on a more limited scale. In approximately one week, the Stratolifters delivered almost 850 tons of supplies to India.

The growing U.S. military involvement in Southeast Asia (SEA) led to an increased use of the KC-135 in that theater. As a prelude to more extensive use of the Stratotanker in operations over Vietnam, four Stratotankers were used to support a small USAF retaliatory strike on communist forces in Laos during June of 1964.

After the Gulf of Tonkin incident in August 1964, U.S. operations in the Vietnam theater were increased. The arrival of KC-135s during early 1965 allowed PACAF KB-50s to be withdrawn. During that same period, SAC established the 4252nd Strategic Wing at Kadena AB, Okinawa, to control tanker operations in SEA. This operation was called *Young Tiger* and during this operation forward bases at Takhli and Don Muang in Thailand were established. By the middle of 1966 a new controlling unit, the 4258th SW, was established at U-Tapao, Thailand.

In-flight refueling proved itself beyond a doubt during Vietnam. The ability of tactical aircraft to take on fuel while airborne greatly increased their capability and versatility, allowing for greater weapons loads and increased endurance.

One of the most vital aspects of tanker operations during the conflict was the "saving" of receiver aircraft. Pilots of battle-damaged aircraft that were losing fuel, rather than having to eject over hostile areas, could link up with a tanker and take on enough fuel to get back to a friendly base, or at least to an safer area for ejection. In some cases, the receiver had incurred fuel system damage and was leaking fuel as fast as the tanker was pumping it in. In these cases, the tanker would, in effect, drag the receiver back to base, transferring fuel all the way. Many pilots were rescued from certain death or capture, and millions of dollars worth of aircraft were saved by the intervention of the KC-135s.

During Vietnam, TAC was still using the probe-and-drogue refueling system on its older aircraft such as the F-100, F-104 and EB-66, meaning that KC-135s tasked with tanking these types had to be equipped with the drogue adapter. This piece of equipment also had to be used when supporting naval aircraft. The Navy had its own tankers such as the KA-3 Skywarrior and KA-6 Intruder, but these were not as capable as the Stratotanker. Later TAC fighter types, such as the F-4 and F-111, were equipped for Boom refueling.

KC-135s flew in support of the 1973 airlift to Israel, during the Yom Kippur War. MAC was running a major resupply effort to Israel, but was hampered by the refusal of landing rights in many nations. At that time, the C-5A was the only heavy airlifter equipped with a refueling receiver, but the crews lacked refueling training. Hurried efforts qualified a number of Galaxy crews for refueling, allowing the airlift to proceed. Receivers were later added to the C-141 fleet as a result of experience gained during the airlift.

Stratotankers based out of England were heavily involved with the support of Operation EL DORADO CANYON, the April 1986 USAF/USN air strike on Libya. During the week prior to the attack, the size of the tanker forces deployed to RAF Mildenhall and Fairford were increased. At one point, the number of KC-135s visible at Mildenhall reached twenty aircraft, in comparison to the usual eleven. These consisted of KC-135A, KC-135Qs and one KC-135E. RAF Fairford had at least ten KC-135s on base, up from the usual seven. In addition to the deployed Stratotankers, at least twenty-two KC-10 Extenders were in the UK.

The first tanker launches for the strike took place between 1800-1900 on 14 April as six KC-135As (callsigns Dobby 31-36) left Mildenhall, along with eleven KC-10s (callsigns Debar 71, 81-82, 84-91). All six Stratotankers returned to RAF Mildenhall between 2130 and 2320, followed by a single KC-10 (Debar 84). At RAF Fairford, two KC-135As (Dobby 61-62) were launched between 1812 and 1832, along with four KC-10s (Debar 51,53-54, and Dobby 63). Two more KC-135As (Dobby 37 and 91) left Mildenhall between 2400 and 0015, followed by four KC-135Qs (Finny 50, 52, 54-55) which left 0100-0300. The latter aircraft, along with three KC-10s (Finny 51,53, 56) supported two SR-71s (Tromp 30-31) which were launched from Mildenhall between 0500-0600. Finny 54 and 55 returned between 0815-0830, while the other Blackbird tankers did not get back until 1210.

On 16 and 17 April, a number of SR-71 flights were made from Mildenhall, presumably to survey the damage done by the raid. Like the Blackbird mission of 15 April, each of these flights involved two SR-71s supported by four KC-135Os and three KC-10s. Additionally, at least one RC-135 mission was flown from Mildenhall on 15 April.

By 22 April, it was apparent that continued hostilities with Libya were unlikely and the tanker force began returning to their U.S. bases. By 25 April, both RAF Fairford and Mildenhall had returned to normal tanker operations.

A KC-135A Stratotanker refuels a pair of F-105G Wild Weasel aircraft on their way to targets in Vietnam. Tanker support was vital during the air war over North Vietnam. (via Larry Davis)

During late July 1990, as tensions over Iraqi troop deployments on the Kuwaiti border increased, the U.S. conducted Operation IVORY JUSTICE in conjunction with the United Arab Emirates. This small exercise entailed the deployment of two KC-135s and a C-141B Starlifter to the Gulf region.

Following the Iraqi invasion of Kuwait on 2 August, the U.S. military began to gear up for possible Middle-East duty. When Saudi Arabia permitted U.S. forces to make use of Saudi bases, Operation DESERT SHIELD began, involving the largest airlift yet mounted, as well as a mass movement of tactical aircraft from the U.S. to the Gulf, both events requiring KC-135 support. Many Stratotanker crews had previously flown from Saudi bases during support of the *Elf One* AWACS deployment. The USAF maintained AWACS aircraft in Saudi Arabia until the arrival of Saudi E-3s.

The huge number of Allied aircraft sent to the Middle East meant that there was a need for a large number of supporting tankers. SAC was to deploy a third of its tanker force in support of Gulf operations. KC-135s and French C-135FRs were joined by SAC KC-10s, Royal Saudi Air Force and USMC KC-130s, RAF VC.10s, Saudi KE-3As, and ANG and AFRes KC-135E units. The ANG and Reserve units participated, both voluntarily and on an activated basis with some units being recalled to active service for unspecified periods of time, while others rotated crews on and off active duty as needed.

Although the TAC deployments and MAC airlift were successful, problems were encountered. For example, MAC's C-141B Starlifter fleet began to experience fatigue problems, so aerial refueling of Starlifters had to be suspended to keep the old but vital airlifters flying.

During the early days of the operation, much of the U.S. airpower in the region was provided by a number of aircraft carriers in the Gulf Of Oman. Because the Navy did not wish to operate in the confines of the Gulf itself, carrier aircraft needed extensive tanker support to increase their loiter time at the far northern end of the Gulf. As a result, Stratotankers fitted with probe and drogue adapters refueled USN aircraft, as well as Allied aircraft fitted with probes. As a result of the Gulf War experience, it is now likely that Stratotankers will be outfitted in the near future with drogue pods, with at least some TAC aircraft being equipped with probes.

Besides the tanker fleet, RC-135s played a major role in gathering intelligence on Iraqi communications and radar systems, allowing Allied planners to devise ways to jam or otherwise circumvent these systems.

The strain of providing DESERT SHIELD with refueling assets led SAC to cut short a B-1B deployment to Guam, as well as terminating the *Giant Voice* bombing competition. The USAF Thunderbirds demonstration team, scheduled to attend the Farnborough Air Show in the U.K., had to keep their F-16s in the United States, as tankers could not be spared to get the team across the Atlantic. Aside from the Gulf itself, tankers also flew from RAF Fairford in support of B-52 bombing operations.

During the war KC-135s and other Allied tankers were, at first, restricted to operations south of the Iraqi border. Stratotankers would eventually fly over southern Iraq itself once Hussein's air force had been neutralized and the anti-aircraft threat reduced. Despite the Stratotanker's lack of ECM equipment (a problem that is being corrected) no KC-135s were brought under attack and there were no losses.

An F-4E Phantom II of the 35th Tactical Fighter Wing waits his turn while his wingman takes on fuel from a Thailand based KC-135A tanker. Most refuelings took place either over Thailand, Laos or over the Gulf of Tonkin. (Via Larry Davis)

A KC-135A (57-2602) of the 7th BW on the ramp at RAF Fairford with a group of KC-10 Extenders just prior to the U.S. raid on Libya. The tankers staged out of England to refuel the F-111s in their flight around France. (Simon Edwards)

A KC-135R refuels a Rockwell International B-1B strategic bomber. Unlike most aircraft, the B-1B has the refueling receptacle mounted forward of the cockpit making it easier for the pilot to position his aircraft for refueling. (USAF)

An AC-130 is refueled by a KC-135E of the 160th Air Refueling Group, Ohio Air National Guard over northern Saudi Arabia during December of 1990. Reserve refueling squadrons were very active during Operation DESERT SHIELD/DESERT STORM. (MAJ Chuck Schmitz, Ohio ANG)

A KC-135A (55-3130) refuels a General Dynamics F-16A while a two-seat F-16B flies the wing position waiting his turn to move into the refueling position. (General Dynamics)

Modern USAF Aircraft from squadron/signal

1024

1049

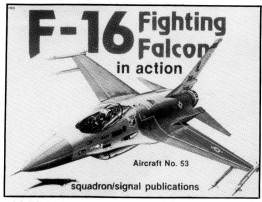

1053

1055

1086

1115

squadron/signal publications